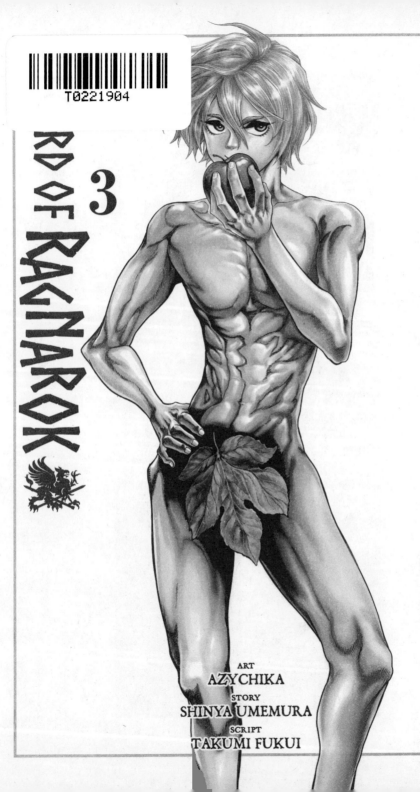

RD OF RAGNAROK

3

ART
AZYCHIKA
STORY
SHINYA UMEMURA
SCRIPT
TAKUMI FUKUI

3

RECORD OF RAGNAROK

CHAPTER 10: EXPULSION FROM PARADISE

...WHAT TOOK PLACE...

...BEFORE HIS EYES.

ARES WOULD LATER RECALL...

I'M ASHAMED TO ADMIT THIS, BUT...

...I'LL BE HONEST.

... SOMEHOW ...

NO, *ALMOST* SIMULTA-NEOUSLY...

...ADAM SIMULTA-NEOUSLY~

...LORD ZEUS'S TECH-NIQUE.

...COPIED...

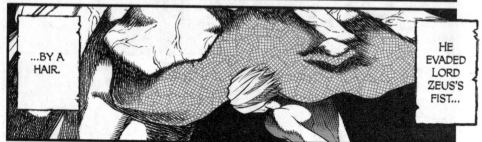

...BY A HAIR.

HE EVADED LORD ZEUS'S FIST...

FWSH

THEN...

GWSHH

HERMES...

...HE CONNECTED WITH HIS OWN.

SH

W F

ARE YOU TELLIN' ME YOU **SAW** IT?!

YOU SAW WHAT I, YOUR BROTHER, THE GOD OF WAR, COULDN'T SEE?!

JOLT

!

...DEAR BROTHER.

THAT'S JUST...

...THE FEELING I GOT...

...WHAT HAP-PENED.

ANYWAY, I HAVE ABSO-LUTELY NO IDEA...

...THAT I'M CERTAIN OF.

BUT THERE IS ONE THING...

TCH TCH

HMPH!

...

I COULD TRAIN FOR A THOUSAND YEARS...

...AND I STILL WOULDN'T BE ABLE TO BEAT THAT HUMAN!

WHO IS THIS, ADAM?!

COPYING A GOD'S TECHNIQUE IS ONE THING, BUT TO ACTUALLY BEAT A GOD...?

HE'S STRONG... TOO STRONG!

WAAA

...OF THE GODS.

HIS HATRED...

I THOUGHT I TOLD YOU. THE SOURCE OF HIS STRENGTH RESIDES IN HIS MOST SINISTER HEART.

...

HATRED...?

GARDEN OF EDEN

AHHH

NOM NOM

...TOGETHER WITH THE ANIMALS IN PARADISE.

ADAM LIVED A VERY COMFORTABLE LIFE...

HEAVEN'S COURT

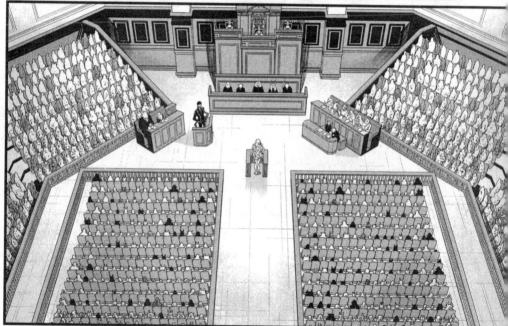

I DID NOT!

I...

BUT IN TRUTH...

PLEASE STOP!

NO!

S-SOME-BODY HELP!

HEH HEH HEH ...

FLAPPA

WHOA! WHAT THE—?!

OH!

ADAM!

SLURP

GIVE IT UP! NO ONE'S COMING TO SAVE YOU!

KONK

ARGH!

TpTpTp

SHOVE

...THE SERPENT TRIED TO MAKE EVE HIS OWN.

RESENTFUL THAT EVE REMAINED FAITHFUL TO HER HUSBAND, ADAM...

CHOMP

I'LL SHOW YOU...

...WHAT HAPPENS WHEN YOU HUMILIATE ME!

THAT BITCH!

THE SENTENCE WAS **EXPULSION FROM PARADISE.**

WHAT'S THIS? WE'RE IN THE MIDDLE OF AN INQUIRY.

?

KRRRK

SWAY

?!

FHOOOM

THP

W— WHAT'S GOING ON?!

WHO—**OM**

...TREE OF KNOWLEDGE OF GOOD AND EVIL?!

FRUIT FROM THE...

HU UHH?!

THIS IS A SACRED PLACE OF JUDGMENT. YOU DON'T BELONG HERE!

WHAT ARE YOU DOING HERE, ADAM?!

MUTTER

HE'S CRAZY!

HE'LL BE CHARGED FOR EVERY ONE HE'S PICKED!

DID HE PICK 'EM ALL?!

MUTTER

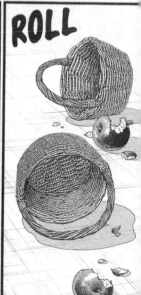

THERE WILL BE NO HAPPY ENDING FOR THOSE WHO BLASPHEME AGAINST THE GODS!

A LITTLE BIRD TOLD ME...

...YOU MADE EVE CRY.

NOW, SEE HERE...

SWP

ZROOSH

...PIECES...!

SPLAT

...

...OUGHTA
STOP YOUR
MISCHIEF.

THAT...

TWK.
TWK.

WHEW

ZEUS HAD ME WORRIED FOR A BIT. BUT ADAM MATCHED UP WELL AGAINST HIM. THINGS WORKED OUT ALL RIGHT.

YES!!

NOW THE SCORE IS EVEN!

PUMP

HEH HEH

...IS HUGE!

BUT MORE IMPORTANTLY, KNOCKING THAT OLD GEEZER OUT SO EARLY...

YAA

ADAM HAS AVENGED HIS BANISH-MENT!

WAY TO GO, FATHER!

TAKE THAT, GODS!

...

I CAN'T STOP LAUGHING!

NO!

BWAHAHA

IT'S NOT OVER.

EEEE!

TWIK

KRIK
KRIK
KRIK

...

AIEE!

HMPH!

PTOK

TRUE, BUT...

I KNEW HE WASN'T DONE!

WAAAA

THE OLD MAN'S BACK!

HE SNAPPED HIS HEAD BACK INTO PLACE!

RAA

WAY TO GO, LORD ZEUS!

YEAH!

...OLD-TIMER.

I WOULDN'T DO THAT...

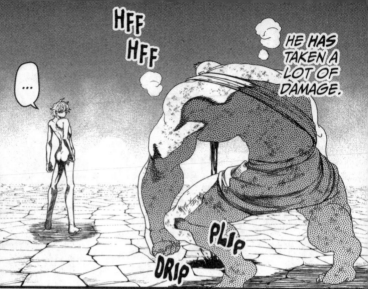

...

HFF HFF

HE HAS TAKEN A LOT OF DAMAGE.

DRIP

PLIP

NOW I KNOW THAT YOU'RE NOT ALL TALK.

HFFF

GWOK

I GET IT, I GET IT...

...ONE MORE THING.

SO, JUST TELL THIS OLD-TIMER...

SHFF

YOU SHOWED ME WHAT YOU CAN DO.

40

YOUR EYES.

I DON'T SEE THE FLAMES OF HATRED TOWARD US GODS IN YOUR EYES.

WHAT'S THE *REAL* REASON...

...YOU CAME OUT HERE TO FIGHT?

WHAT IS IT WITH YOU GUYS?

HATRED?

REVENGE?

SIGH ...

YOU TOO?

THERE IS NO "WHY."

I DON'T NEED ANY OF THAT.

DOES ANYONE NEED A *REASON*...

...TO PROTECT THEIR OWN CHILDREN?

CHAPTER 10 ~ END

SIXTH OF
THE 12
OLYMPIANS

ARES

WHY RISK ONE'S LIFE TO FIGHT?

ONE DOES NOT *NEED* A REASON.

HIS ENORMOUS BENEVOLENCE...

THEIR FATHER'S WORDS...

...FILLED THE HEARTS OF HIS CHILDREN.

...EVERY HUMAN THERE, IN THEIR OWN WAY...

...UNBIDDEN...

...AND ALL AT ONCE...

AND WITHOUT ANYONE TAKING THE LEAD...

THE RICH, THE POOR, THE GOOD, THE BAD...

POLITICIANS, CRIMINALS...

THERE WAS NO SEX, RACE, ETHNICITY, NOR RELIGION...

THEY ALL PRAYED FOR THE SAME THING.

FOR THE FIRST TIME IN THEIR HISTORY, HUMANITY CAME TOGETHER AS ONE.

ADAM'S VICTORY!

NOT BAD.

YOU'VE WON OVER THE CROWD.

HMPH...

HFF HFF

HFF

...

TWK TWK

YOU SHOULD'VE STAYED DOWN.

SIGH...

YOU DO REALIZE...

...YOU'LL DIE THIS TIME, RIGHT?

I'LL GIVE YOU THAT!

Y-YOU ARE STRONG...

GRIP GRIP

TRMBL TRMBL

TRMBL

NOW I KNOW THAT'S NOT JUST TALK.

H...

HEH HEH...

...

MAYBE THE OLD GEEZER HAS FINALLY GONE SENILE.

....

WHAT'S HE TRYING T'DO?

TMP

TMP

HUH?!

YOU DON'T GET IT.

HSSST

...

HILDE!

LORD ZEUS IS...

...

THAT OLD GEEZER!

BUT WITH ALL THE INJUR- IES HE'S SUFFERED, I'D SAY HE'S GOT SIX MINUTES AT BEST.

IF HE WERE IN PEAK CONDITION, HE COULD LAST A DOZEN MINUTES IN THAT FORM.

WHAT IS THAT FORM?!

...

W-WHAT PRESENCE!

...DESTROY THE HEAVENS!

THMP

THMP

DO NOT...

ADAM, WHO HAD NOT YET TAKEN A DEFENSIVE STANCE...

...REFLEXIVELY BROUGHT UP HIS HANDS AT THE SIGHT OF THIS MYSTERI- OUS AND SINISTER CREATURE.

HSSS

HSSS

...AND STORING IMMENSE POWER, WERE SCREAMING IN PAIN.

ZEUS'S MUSCLES, COM- PRESSED TO THEIR LIMITS...

BWUP

BWUP

BWUP

THE ONE

...BEST STRAIGHT RIGHT!

UNBELIEV-ABLE!

ADAM HAS EVEN COPIED LORD ZEUS'S...

CHAPTER 11 ~ END

PLIP

CHAPTER 12: OVERFLOWING LOVE

...LORD ZEUS WAS JUST RECKLESSLY THROWING PUNCHES.

I DIDN'T NOTICE UNTIL NOW BECAUSE IT LOOKED LIKE...

OVER-HEATED ?!

...ONE-HIT-ONE-KILL PUNCH!

BUT IN REALITY, EACH ONE OF THEM WAS AN INESCAP-ABLE...

DURING THAT EX-CHANGE ...

IN OTHER WORDS ...

HE'S CLOSE TO HIS LIMIT TOO.

IT'S IMPOSSIBLE TO KEEP THROWING PUNCHES LIKE THAT.

H-HIS MUSCLES ARE ABOUT TO TEAR!

L-LORD ZEUS?!

THEY'RE LIKE WINE GLASSES.

SHNG

THINK OF IT LIKE THIS...

GLUK

IT'S A CONTEST OF ENDUR-ANCE.

GLUK

GLUK

GLUK

THERE'S ONLY SO MUCH WINE— OR *LIFE*— YOU CAN POUR INTO ONE BEFORE IT OVERFLOWS.

RIPPLE

SURFACE TENSION IS THE ONLY THING KEEPING THEM FROM SPILLING OVER.

OOOO... THAT WAS CLOSE! ♡

THE SLIGHTEST DISRUPTION...

...OVER-FLOW.

...AND THE GLASSES WILL...

BLP BLP

BLP

88

BLPP

HOW-
EVER...

THM P

AGAINST
ZEUS, WHO
CONTINUED
THROWING...

...LETHAL
BLOWS...

KSHH

KSHH

KSHH

...ADAM STOOD HIS GROUND!

WH

...EACH BLOW WITH DIVINE REPLICATION.

AM

HE COUNTERED...

THEY'RE BOTH HANGING ON.

HMM...

...OF THE BATTLE'S LETHALITY.

HUSH

HUSH

...AWED BY THE BEAUTY...

HUSH

HUSH

THE HUMANS AND THE GODS WERE *ALL* ON THEIR FEET...

SEE THAT, ADAM?! YOUR ATTACK AIN'T NOTHIN' TO LORD ZEUS!

G·F·O·C!

WHMP

LORD ZEUS!

G·F·O·C!

FATHER!

THMP

ADAM!

FATHER!

GIVE IT UP, ZEUS!

YOU BETTER NOT QUIT NOW!

DO YA HEAR ME?!

DM

OLD MAN...

DM

...THAT FILLED VALHALLA ARENA...

AMID THE FRENZY...

WHO WAS THAT?

...ONE PERSON SAW WHAT WAS COMING BEFORE ANYONE ELSE.

IT WAS ADAM HIMSELF.

...EVEN GREAT EVENTS...

IN THIS WORLD...

...THE MOST TRIVIAL CAUSES.

...ARE SET OFF BY...

THEY ALL START...

EVEN REVO-LUTIONS AND WARS.

GOUT. HAY FEVER.

...FROM ONE LITTLE THING.

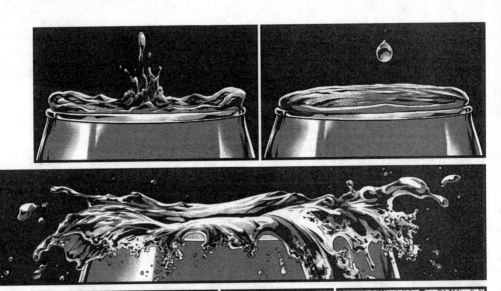

THA DA DUM

HE'S A HUMAN PUNCHING BAG!

WHAT'S HAPPENED TO ADAM?! HE'S ON THE DEFENSIVE!

ALL HE CAN DO IS DEFEND.

...

HE'S...

H-HILDE! ADAM...

...SEE ANYTHING ANYMORE.

I DOUBT HE CAN EVEN...

...OVER-FLOWED FIRST.

SLURP

SO, ADAM...

SPSH

PLIP

PLIP

AWWW...

...TOUGH SON OF A BITCH.

HE'S ONE...

WHMP

BUT MAN...!

YEAH, HE'S TOAST.

WHEW! IT'S OVER THIS TIME FOR SURE.

...OVER.

IT'S...

BAK

BAK

SOME-
WHERE...

...A
BABY IS
CRYING.

DON'T
CRY.

IT'S
OKAY.

...DADDY
WILL...

IF
ANYONE
SCARES
YOU...

...TAKE CARE OF THEM.

111

THEIR FATHER WAS STILL TRYING TO GRASP THAT LAST STRAW OF VICTORY!

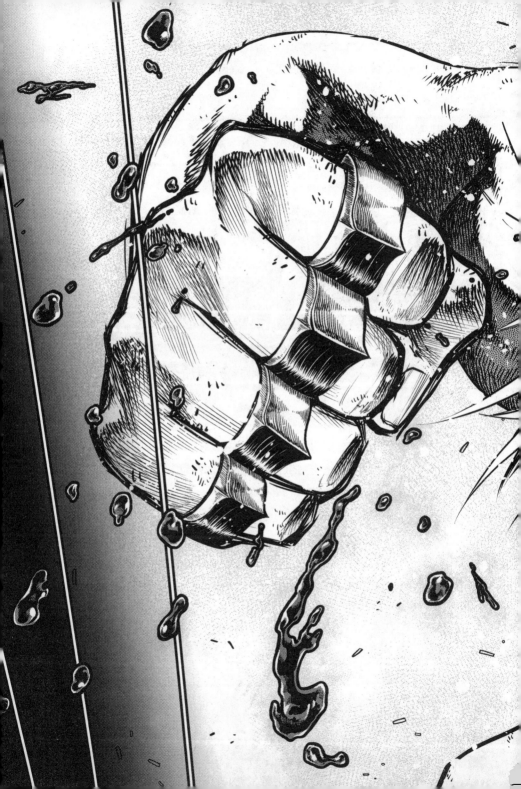

THE END...

...CAME SUDDENLY.

124

HE...

...LONG BEFORE I FELL.

HE TOOK HIS LAST BREATH...

WHAT ?

HMPH! YOU JUST NOW REALIZED THAT?

ACTUALLY... NOT ONLY THAT...

YET HE STAYED ON HIS FEET.

...EVEN IN DEATH.

HE'S DONE.

...HE KEPT SWINGING HIS FISTS...

...LORD ZEE-UUU-SS!

THE WINNER OF THE SECOND ROUND OF RAGNAROK IS...

ZEUS VS. ADAM
MATCH DURATION: 7 MIN., 13 SEC.
DECIDING TECHNIQUE: FIST STRIKE
WINNER: ZEUS

CHAPTER 12 ~ END

SEVENTH
OLDEST
OF THE
13 VALKYRIE
SISTERS

REGINLEIF

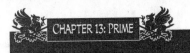

CHAPTER 13: PRIME

TWO CONSECUTIVE LOSSES.

...A HOPELESS SITUATION.

IT SEEMED TO BE...

TMP

THMP

TMP

... WAS HANGING THEIR HEAD!

YET NO ONE...

...A GREAT LEGACY TO HIS CHILDREN.

EVEN IN DEATH, ADAM HAD LEFT...

CHOK

TMP TMP TMP

WHUMP

HNNG

CALM DOWN.

GEIR...

HILDE! WHAT'S GOING ON?!

LEIF KNEW THE CONSEQUENCES OF THESE BATTLES.

SIGH...

DON'T CRY...

MMPH

HUG

I COULDN'T DO ANYTHING FOR HER.

BUT...I COULDN'T EVEN SAY GOODBYE.

HRIST...

SQUEEZE

GEIR...

GRRRIP

OH...

OWWW!

GRP GRP GRP

...DWELLING INSIDE HER.

HRIST IS THE ONLY VALKYRIE TO HAVE **TWO** POWERS...

TH-THAT'S RIGHT...

...

HRIST

...MEANS...

HER NAME...

THE QUAKING ONE
AND
THE ROARING ONE

GNAW
NOM
CHOMP
CHOMP
CHEW
NOM
NOM

NOM
NOM
NOM

I... I WISH YOU'D CALM DOWN, HRIST.

HE BEAT ONE OF MY BEST HUMANS!

SHIT, SHIT, SHIT! THAT DIRTY OLD GEEZER!

THAT'S WHAT SHE DOES WHEN SHE'S STRESSED!

GAH! SHE'S BINGE EATING SALMIAK!

DRIB BL

BY THE WAY, THAT PIE IS HILDE'S RECIPE. IT'S SHOCKINGLY VILE.

SALMIAK
A NORTHERN EUROPEAN CONFECTIONERY MADE FROM AMMONIUM CHLORIDE AND LICORICE. INFAMOUS (ACCORDING TO SOME) AS THE MOST AWFUL-TASTING OF ALL SWEETS.

WE HAVE TO... WE ABSOLUTELY MUST WIN THE NEXT ROUND!

IF WE LOSE THE NEXT ONE, THAT'LL BE THREE IN A ROW!

NOM

MUNCH

VRRING♪

GULP

!!

FWSH

TKATKA

KRASH

TEK TEK TEK

H-HILDE...? IS EVERY-THING ALL RIGHT?

PTOK

?!

THE GODS' REPRESENTATIVE FOR ROUND 3 IS POSEIDON

FOR ROUND 3 POSEIDON !!!

...AFTER LORD ZEUS?!

P-P-POSEI-DON...

IT'S ONLY ROUND THREE. WHY DO THEY KEEP SENDING OUT THEIR HEAVY-WEIGHTS...?

P-POSEI-DON...?

THEY WANT OUR BACKS UP AGAINST THE WALL.

WHAT'RE WE GONNA DO, HILDE?

... TAKKA

TEK TEK

OF ALL THE GODS, WHY *HIM*?! ARE WE GONNA BE OKAY?!

POSEIDON IS LORD ZEUS'S OLDER BROTHER!

HE HAS TO BE SUPER-STRONG!

ARE THEY TRYING TO GO FOR A SWEEP?!

YONK

WOULD YOU MIND...

...ZIPPING IT FOR A WHILE?

GEIR.

HILDE...!

TAP

...I MAY ACCIDENTALLY CHOP OFF YOUR HEAD.

OTHER-WISE...

HER MOOD SWINGS ARE EVEN WORSE THAN HRIST'S!

SHE SAYS THE SCARIEST THINGS WITH A SMILE!

YIKES

Y-YES, MA'AM!

OUR BACKS ARE ALREADY UP AGAINST THE WALL!!

DAMN IT...

FLK FLK

SWP SWP

SWP SWP SWP

FLK FLK

FLK

WHO...?

WHO COULD POSSIBLY...

MICHEL NOSTRADAMUS

WHFF

QIN SHI HUAI...

WHFF

KING LEONIDAS

WHFF

FWSH

?!

...OPPOSE POSEIDON?!

THE ZEUS OF THE SEAS!

SL

A_P?!

RMMMBL

WHERE'D HE COME FROM?!

?!

I SHALL GO.

Sasaki Kojiro /Japan

NAME
Sasaki Kojiro /Japan

NAME
Sasaki Kojiro /Japan

A-ARE YOU...

SASAKI KOJIRO?

...AN OLD MAN.

YOU'RE KINDA SHRIV-ELED. KINDA LIKE...

YOU LOOK DIFFERENT FROM OUR RECORDS.

NAME
Sasaki Kojiro /Japan

WHY DO YOU LOOK THE WAY YOU DO?!

WHMP

SHE'S RIGHT!

TIP...

...IN THEIR PRIME REGARD-LESS OF THEIR AGE WHEN THEY DIED?

I THOUGHT THE SOULS SUMMONED TO RAGNAROK APPEARED...

ADAM!

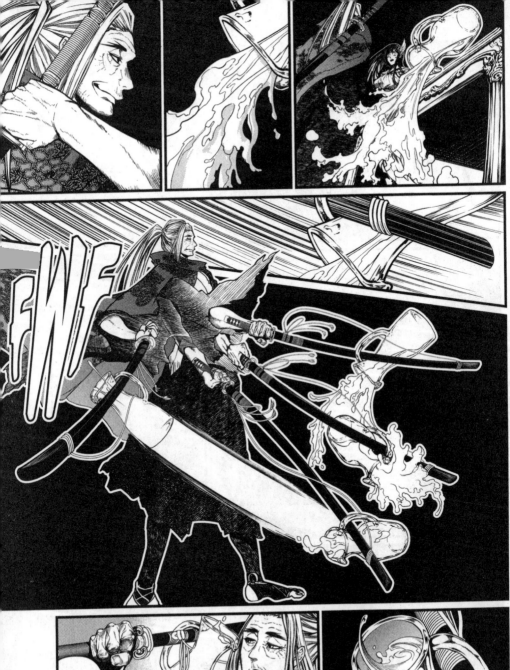

HEY...

SWK **SPSH**

GLUG GLUG

ICK!

HE'S EATING OFF THE FLOOR?!

THIS ISN'T BAD EITHER.

I DON'T WHAT IT IS... BUT IT'S PRETTY GOOD.

MAYBE HE ISN'T SASAKI KOJIRO!

HOW CAN HE EAT THAT?!

NOM NOM NOM NOM NOM

COW'S MILK, HUH? MMM... IT'S GOOD.

HMM?

TNK

BUT...

HE'S NOT HOW I IMAGINED.

WHAT A FEAST!

MMM...

PAK PAK

SKCH
SKCH

...THE REAL DEAL!

HE IS DEFINITELY...

CATCHING THAT PITCHER OF MILK WITHOUT SPILLING A DROP...!

HE UNDOUBTEDLY HAS THE SKILLS OF A MASTER!

HEH.

TUG

...NEVER ENDS.

KOJIRO'S EVOLUTION...

ZWF

IN THE 400 YEARS SINCE I ASCENDED TO HEAVEN...

...I'VE CONTINUED TO HONE MY SKILLS WITH THE SWORD...

...

SHIVR

CHATTER CHATTER MUTTER

CHAPTER 14: TYRANT OF THE SEAS

I CAN'T WAIT FOR THE NEXT ROUND!

YEAH. I HAVEN'T BEEN THIS EXCITED FOR A FEW MILLENNIA!

MAN, THAT WAS A HELLUVA BATTLE! THAT HUMAN PUT UP A BETTER FIGHT THAN I EXPECTED!

WHAT'S UP WITH THE ARENA FOR ROUND THREE?

BUT DUDE...

KYA

KYA

SPSHH

THE TYRANT OF THE SEAS!

OOOH

TH-THE WATER...

...IS PARTING!

SOMEONE WITH AN EVEN WORSE SENSE OF HUMOR THAN ODIN.

HMM... POSEIDON, HUH?

SHF

...

BOW

HUSH

SHH

NNG

AND ....!

POSEI-DON... ZEUS'S OLDER BROTH-ER...

EVEN HIS FELLOW GODS FEAR HIM.

GULP

... THAT *THIS* IS THE ULTIMATE SWORDS-MAN!

I PRO-CLAIM...

KTNk

OR HIS THIRST FOR VENGEANCE AGAINST THE GODS WHO LOVED MUSASHI MORE THAN HIM?!

... THE *TSUMABE GAESHI* ?!

IS IT HIS SIG-NATURE TECH-NIQUE...

?!

BUT HOW CAN A MAN WHO TASTED DEFEAT BE THE ULTIMATE, YOU ASK?

SMIRK

HUMANITY'S GREATEST LOSER

MUTTER MUTTER

THERE'S NO WAY HE CAN WIN! WHAT'RE THEY THINKING?!

HUH? *THAT OLD MAN'S* REPRESENTING HUMANITY?

THA DUM

WHY IS THE MAN WHO *LOST* TO MY FATHER REPRESENTING US?!

GRRR

MIYAMOTO IORI
ADOPTED SON OF
MIYAMOTO MUSASHI

I *OBJECT* TO THIS SELECTION!

THIS IS UNACCEPTABLE!

PEOPLE!

AM I WRONG?!

SHF

THE BOOK OF FIVE RINGS, WRITTEN BY MY FATHER AND CONSIDERED A SACRED BOOK OF MARTIAL ARTS, IS *PROOF* OF THAT!

THE TITLE OF HUMANITY'S ULTIMATE SWORDSMAN BELONGS TO MY FATHER, MIYAMOTO MUSASHI!

IT WAS MUSASHI WHO DEFEATED ME.

YOSHIOKA SEIJURO
SWORD INSTRUCTOR FOR THE ASHIKAGA SHOGUNATE

HMPH! NO. YOU'RE RIGHT.

HOWEVER, I WONDER HOW MUSASHI HIMSELF FEELS ABOUT THIS.

YES, INDEED...

HOZOIN INSHUN
HOZOIN STYLE SPEAR MASTER

...

MIYAMOTO MUSASHI
MASTER OF THE
NITEN ICHIRYU STYLE

...

THE HUMAN CROWD SEEMS CONFUSED BY THIS SELECTION...

...HILDE.

MUTTER

CHATTER

WE HAVE TO BELIEVE...

KLIK

SWSHHH

...IN KO-JIRO'S...

...CONTINUED EFFORTS...

SHNNG...

SWF

...TO MASTER THE SWORD!

184

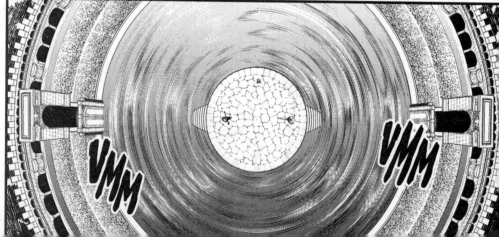

HE'S AN INTERESTING CHOICE.

WHO... WHO IS THAT HUMAN?!

...

GRIN

LOOKS LIKE HUMANITY...

HMM...

...SURPRISES IN STORE FOR US.

...STILL HAS SOME...

RIGHT, FATHER?

HMPH! NO NEED TO BE SURPRISED! IT'S SIMPLY SASAKI'S TRICK!

DID THAT OLD MAN DO THIS?

HEY... THE WATER'S SO STILL NOW.

GRR

PLUP...

PEERLESS UNDER THE HEAVENS

RECORD OF RAGNAROK

VOLUME 3
VIZ Signature Edition

Art by **Azychika**
Story by **Shinya Umemura**
Script by **Takumi Fukui**

Translation / Joe Yamazaki
English Adaptation / Stan!
Touch-Up Art & Lettering / Mark McMurray
Design / Julian (JR) Robinson
Editor / Mike Montesa

Shumatsu no Walkure
©2017 by AZYCHIKA AND SHINYA UMEMURA AND TAKUMI FUKUI/COAMIX
Approved No. ZCW-123W
First Published in Japan in Monthly Comic ZENON by COAMIX, Inc.
English translation rights arranged with COAMIX Inc., Tokyo
through Tuttle-Mori Agency, Inc., Tokyo

Printed in Canada

Published by VIZ Media, LLC
P.O. Box 77010
San Francisco, CA 94107

10 9 8 7 6 5 4 3 2 1
First printing, July 2022

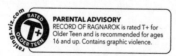

PARENTAL ADVISORY
RECORD OF RAGNAROK is rated T+ for
Older Teen and is recommended for ages
16 and up. Contains graphic violence.

viz.com

vizsignature.com

IN THE ORIGINAL CLASSIC MANGA set in a postapocalyptic wasteland ruled by savage gangs, a hero appears to bring justice to the guilty. This warrior named Ken holds the deadly secrets of a mysterious martial art known as Hokuto Shinken—the Divine Fist of the North Star!

Story by **BURONSON**   Art by **TETSUO HARA**

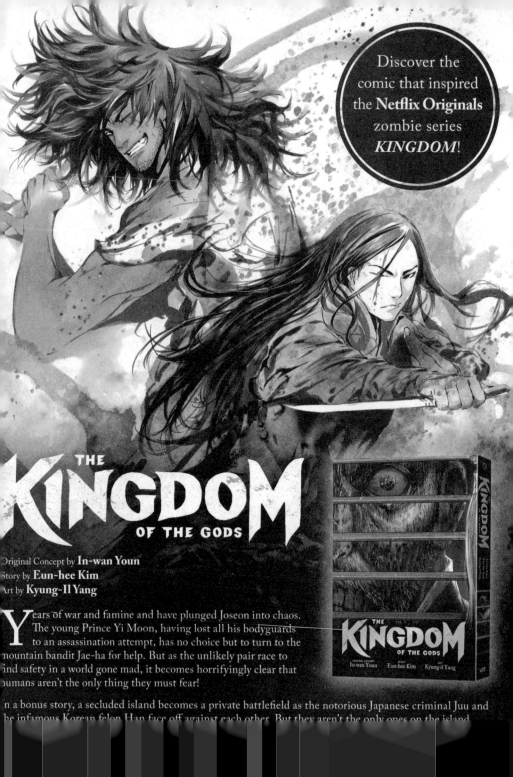

THE KINGDOM OF THE GODS

Original Concept by **In-wan Youn**
Story by **Eun-hee Kim**
Art by **Kyung-Il Yang**

Years of war and famine and have plunged Joseon into chaos. The young Prince Yi Moon, having lost all his bodyguards to an assassination attempt, has no choice but to turn to the mountain bandit Jae-ha for help. But as the unlikely pair race to find safety in a world gone mad, it becomes horrifyingly clear that humans aren't the only thing they must fear!

In a bonus story, a secluded island becomes a private battlefield as the notorious Japanese criminal Juu and the infamous Korean felon Han face off against each other. But they aren't the only ones on the island.

THE KINGDOM OF THE GODS

ORIGINAL CONCEPT
In-wan Youn
STORY
Eun-hee Kim
ART
Kyung-il Yang

VIZ

MOBILE SUIT GUNDAM THUNDERBOLT

In the Universal Century year 0079, the space colony known as Side 3 proclaims independence as the Principality of Zeon and declares war on the Earth Federation. One year later, they are locked in a fierce battle for the Thunderbolt Sector, an area of space scarred by the wreckage of destroyed colonies. Into this maelstrom of destruction go two veteran Mobile Suit pilots: the deadly Zeon sniper Daryl Lorenz, and Federation ace Io Fleming. It's the beginning of a rivalry that can end only when one of them is destroyed.

STORY AND ART
YASUO OHTAGAKI
ORIGINAL CONCEPT BY
HAJIME YATATE
AND YOSHIYUKI TOMINO

viz media
viz.com

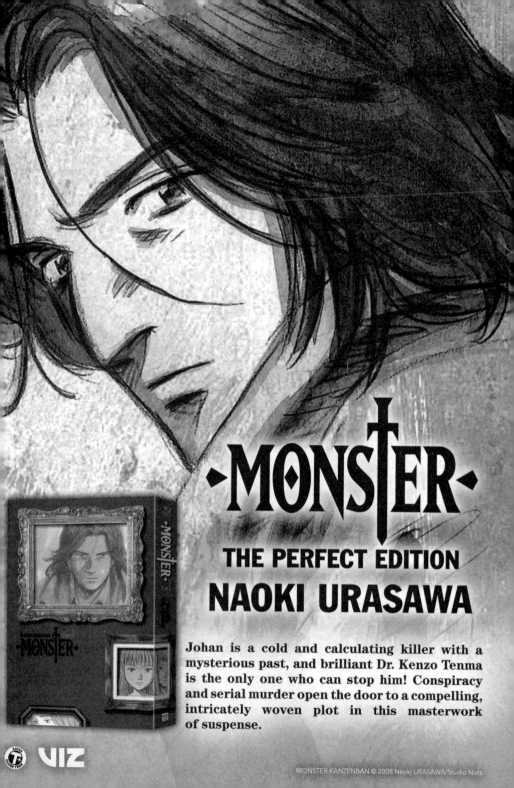

·MONSTER·

THE PERFECT EDITION
NAOKI URASAWA

Johan is a cold and calculating killer with a mysterious past, and brilliant Dr. Kenzo Tenma is the only one who can stop him! Conspiracy and serial murder open the door to a compelling, intricately woven plot in this masterwork of suspense.

REMINA

JUNJI ITO'S CHILLING SCI-FI MASTERWORK *REMINA* PITS THE CHAOS OF THE COSMOS AGAINST THE CRUELTY OF HUMANITY IN THIS DELUXE HARDCOVER.

OU'RE READING IT
WRONG!

KORD OF
AGNAROK

...eads right to left starting
...n the upper-right corner.
...panese is read from right
...left, meaning that action,
...ound effects, and word-
...oon order are completely
...ersed from English order.

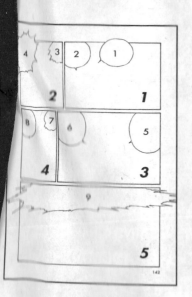

142